GRADE **03**

CLASSICAL GUITAR

Pieces for Trinity College London
Exams 2020–2023

Published by
Trinity College London Press Ltd
trinitycollege.com

Registered in England
Company no. 09726123

Printed in England by Caligraving Ltd

French Dance (Tourdion)

Pierre Attaignant
(c.1494-1551)

In the exam, play the repeat.

Valse

no. 21 from *École de guitare*, op. 241

Ferdinando Carulli
(1770-1841)

Study in C

no. 6 from *Introduction à l'étude de la guitare*, op. 60

Fernando Sor
(1778-1839)

Andantino

from *Le papillon*, op. 50

Mauro Giuliani
(1781–1829)

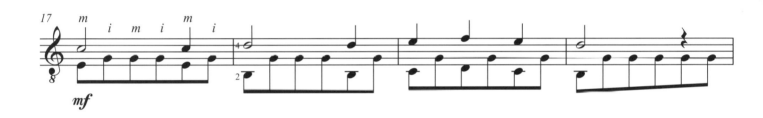

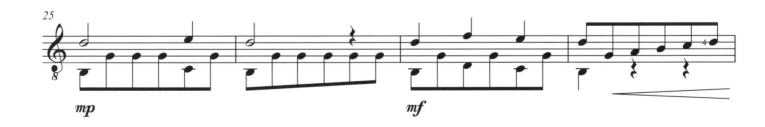

6

Allegretto in D major

Matteo Carcassi
(1792–1853)

Grasshopper Guiro

David Cottam
(b. 1951)

*⤢ Play behind the nut with the back of your left-hand thumb nail or finger tip to make a zingy sound.

Funky Juan

Nicholas Powlesland
(b. 1965)

*Percussive tap of all strings with a flat hand over the soundhole.

The Firth of Lorn

Gary Ryan
(b. 1969)

Kurpie Étude

Tatiana Stachak
(b. 1973)

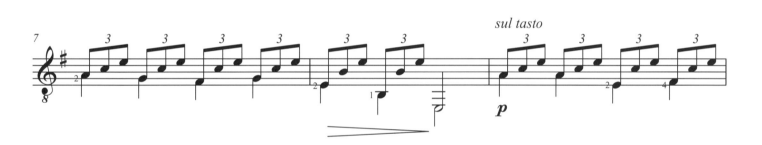

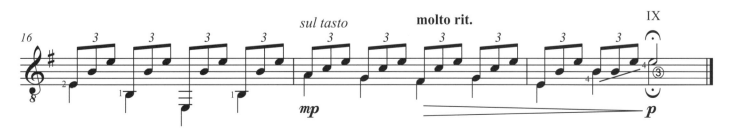

Marshmallow Cocoa

Martin Fogel
(b. 1974)

[The page has been left blank to facilitate page turns]

Album Leaf

Edvard Grieg
(1843-1907)
arr. Powlesland

Chorinho

Trad.
arr. Rivoal

The Coasts of High Barbary

Trad.

arr. Sanderson

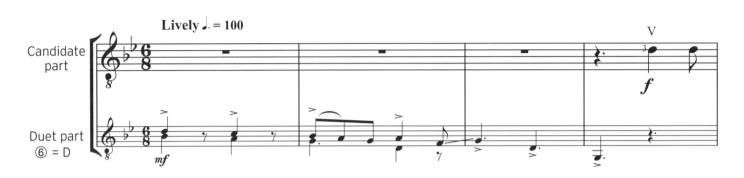

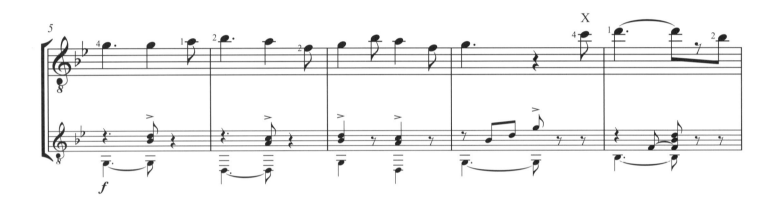

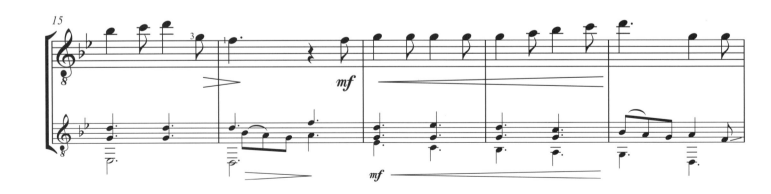